CANDLELIGHT

Art & Logic Therapy

Brain Games

Peace, Comfort and Mental Clarity Through the Psalms

Book 6

NAME: _____

Date: _____

Rest in the Lord
and wait patiently
for Him...

Psalm 37:7

Brain Fog Therapy By Sarah Janisse Brown

Inspired by Dyslexia Games Series C to sharpen the minds
of individuals suffering from clouded thinking.

The Thinking Tree Publishing Company, LLC

FUNSchooling.com

PREPARATION:

- Create a calm environment by reducing distractions and setting the mood.

- Enjoy a cup of tea, coffee, water or green lemonade!

- Have coloring supplies and a fine point black pen ready to use. Use a 08 size professional liner pen for best results, if you would like to match the artist's work.

SCHEDULING OPTIONS:

A. Use 2 pages per day, 6 or 7 days a week.

B. Use 3 pages per day, 4 days per week.

C. Use ten pages per week, any number of days.

INSTRUCTIONS:

Look at each page and decide what is missing. Add the missing parts. Finish the pattern, solve the puzzle, use logic and creativity to complete the picture. Add color as you relax and listen to peaceful music. Coloring gives your brain time to process the therapy. Some pages need color, others do not. It's up to you.

HOW THE GAMES WORK:

The pages include highly detailed drawing activities, number games, word and letter games, and logic puzzles. The games were originally created to create new connections in the brains of dyslexic students. These same connections can help anyone to create new mental pathways for optimum brain function and healthy synapses.

The idea is simple. When you do a new activity your brain is forced to create new pathways. These activities will be unfamiliar to your brain at first. Some pages may seem simple, some may seem confusing and complicated. The idea is to give your brain a workout as you combine creativity, logic, symbols, literacy, and problem solving in a fresh way.

CREATE AN ENVIRONMENT OF NOURISHMENT AND PEACE

Do what it takes to create an environment where you can thrive.

Choose at least two of these prompts each day to help you set the stage for focus and calm. Once you have made a positive change in your surroundings you may begin.

Those that be planted
in the house of the
Lord shall flourish...
Psalm 92:12

Add your own words and complete the drawings...

Listen to inspiring music as you add color...

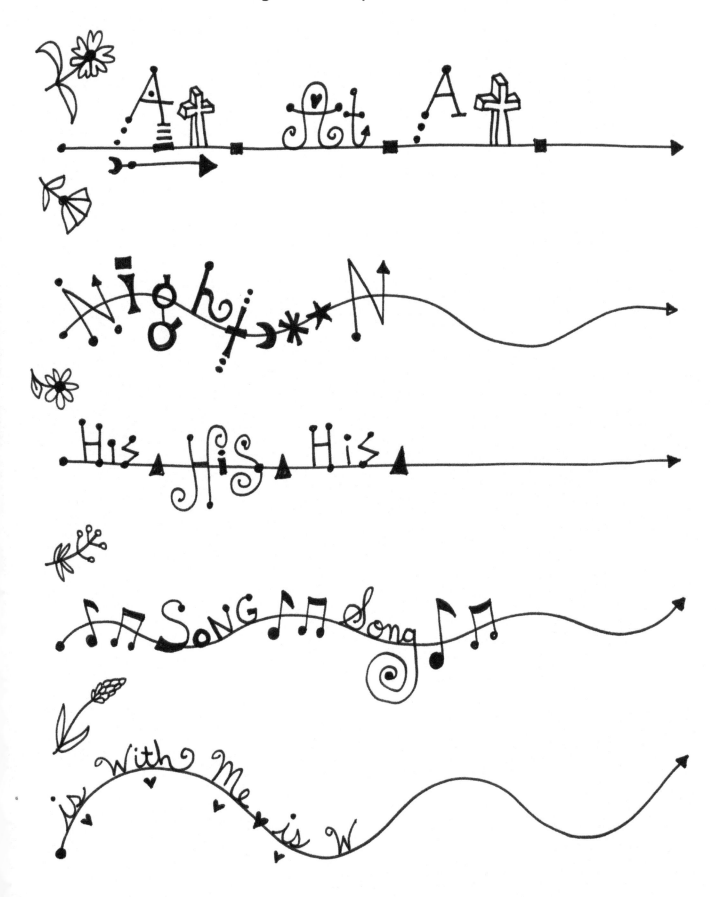

Complete the drawings...

Complete the patterns and drawings...

Use logic to finish the verse...

Use logic to complete the pictures...

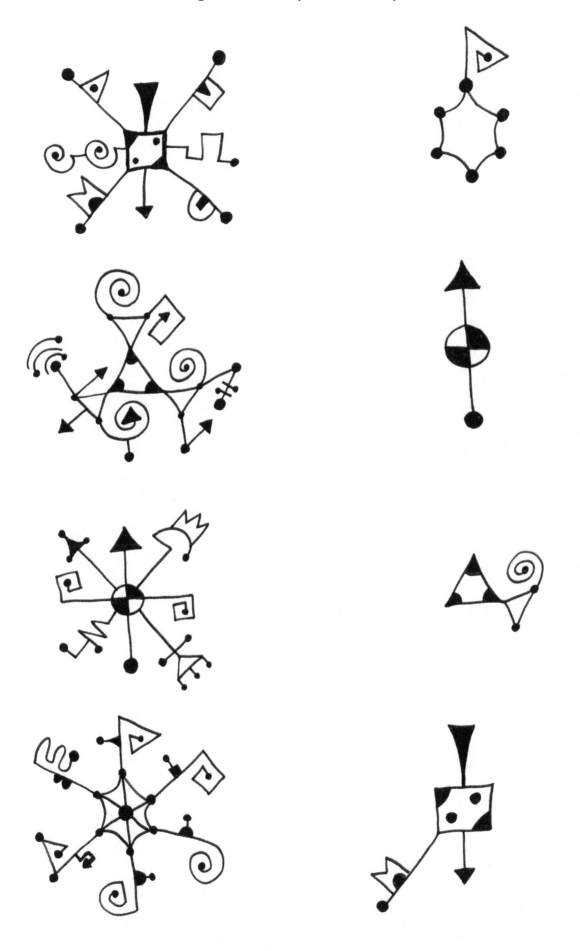

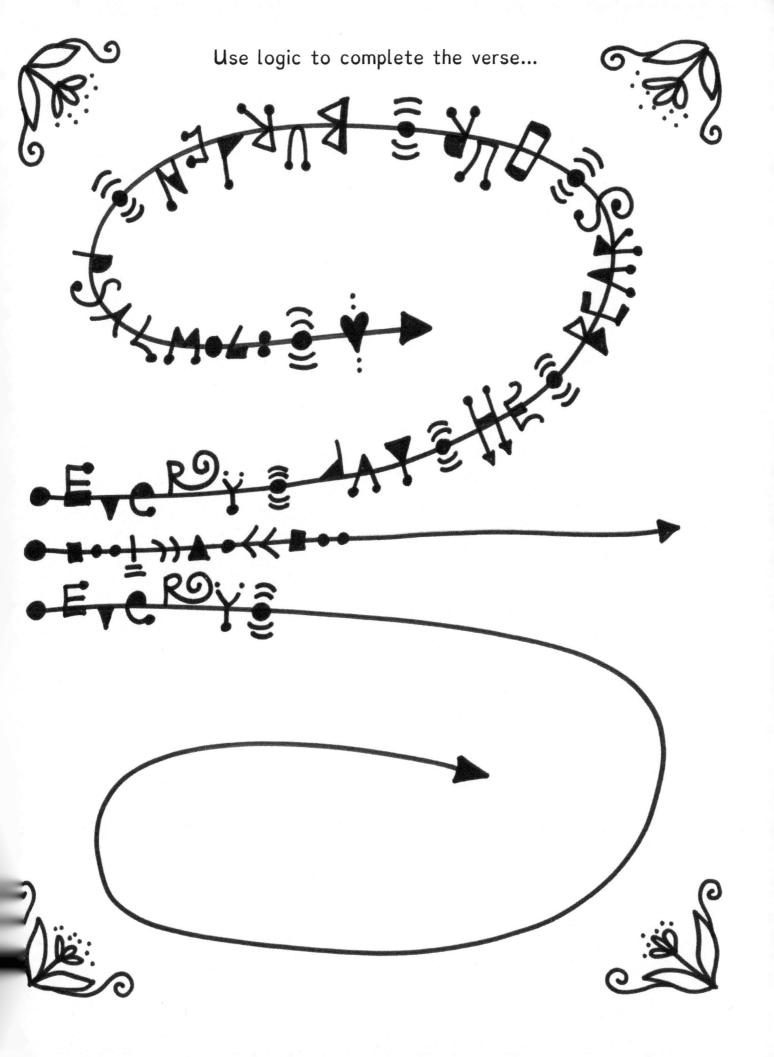

Add color, butterflies and bugs...

Psalm 51

Create in me a clean Heart, God;

Renew a RESOLUTE Spirit in me.

Use logic to draw the missing parts...

Use logic to draw the missing parts...

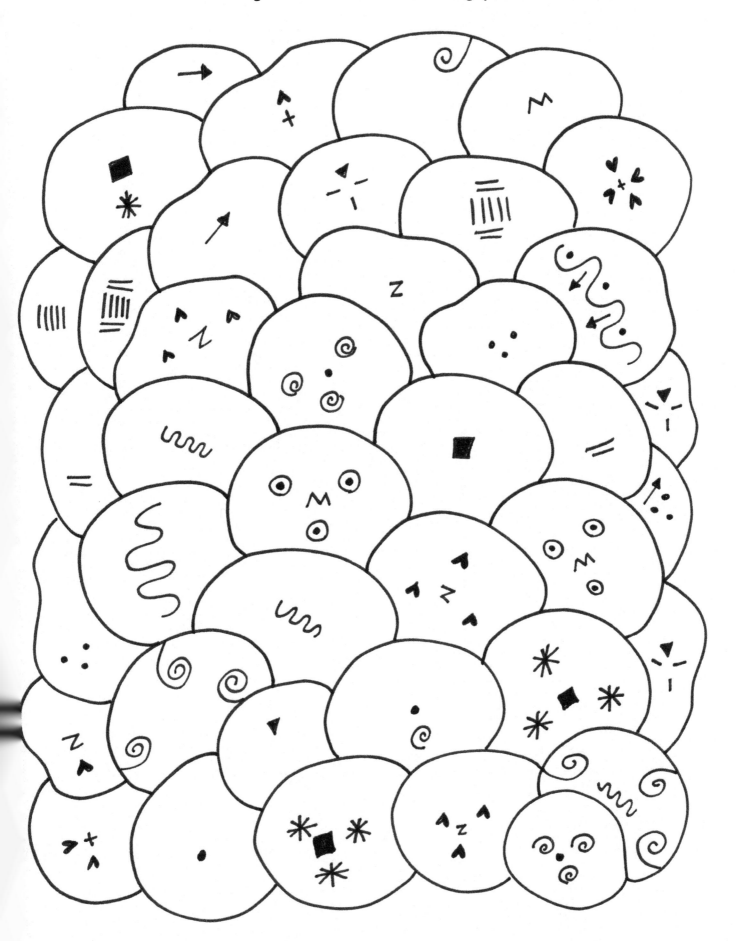

Add words to each leaf and stone...

Add color as you listen to beautiful music...

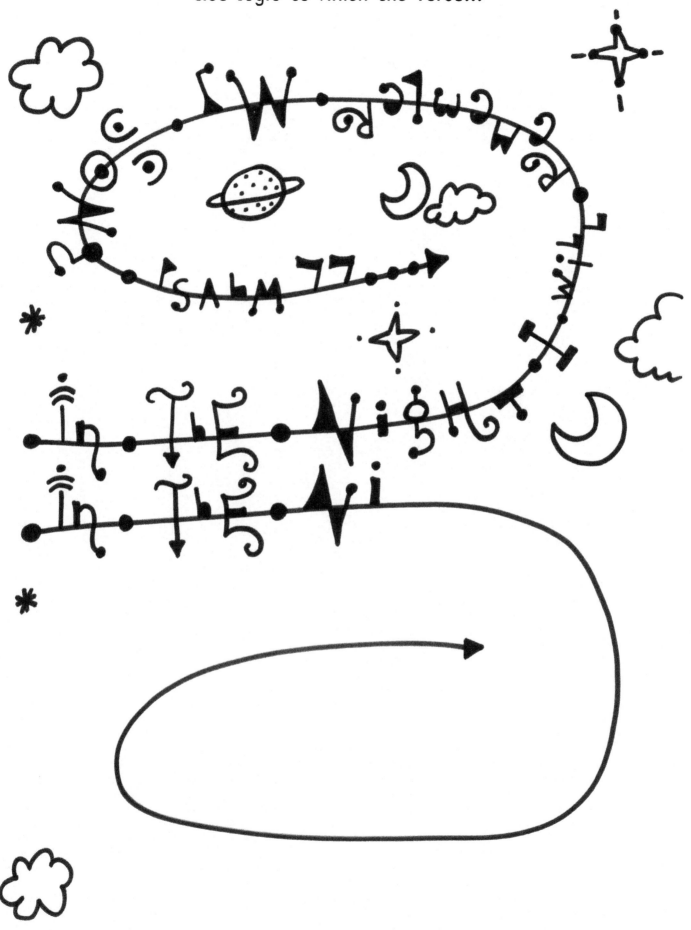

PSALM 77...

In The Night

In The Ni

Add color and complete the drawings...

Meditate on these words as you add color...

My God is my Strength and my Shield in Him my heart trusted and I am helped.

→→→ PSALM 28 ←←←

Draw the missing letters...

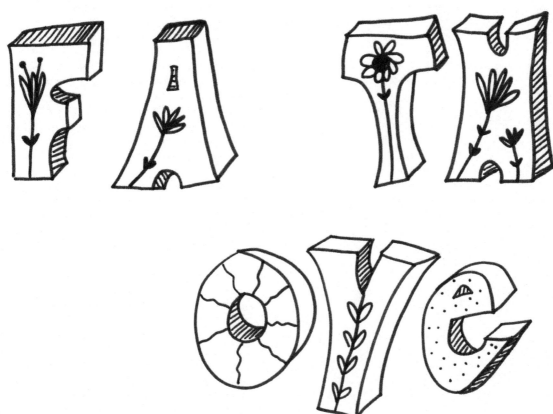

Use logic to complete the verse...

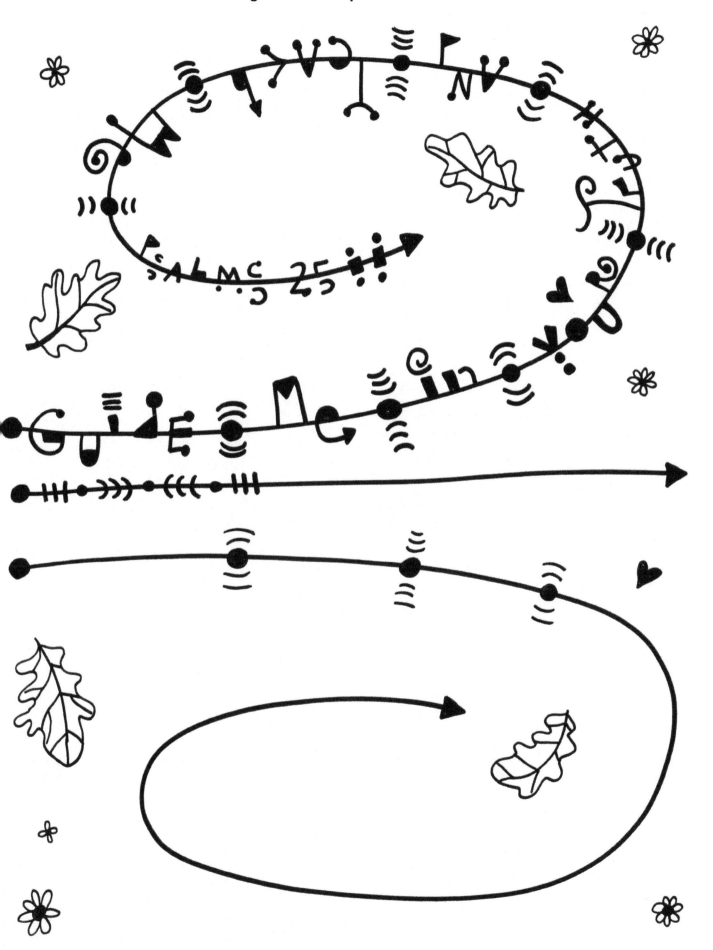

Use logic and creativity as you work through the rest of the pages...

FROM ETERNITY TO... FUTURE
PAST
ETERNITY
f
E
f
p

FUTURE

PSALM 41

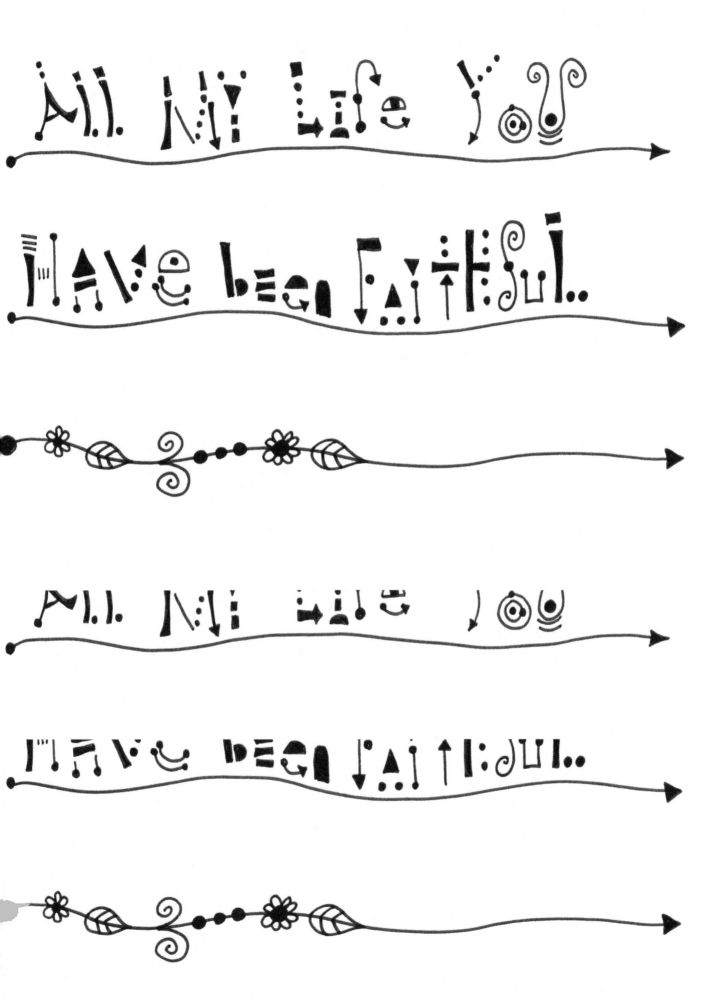

All My Life You

Have been Faithful..

All My Life You

Have been Faithful..

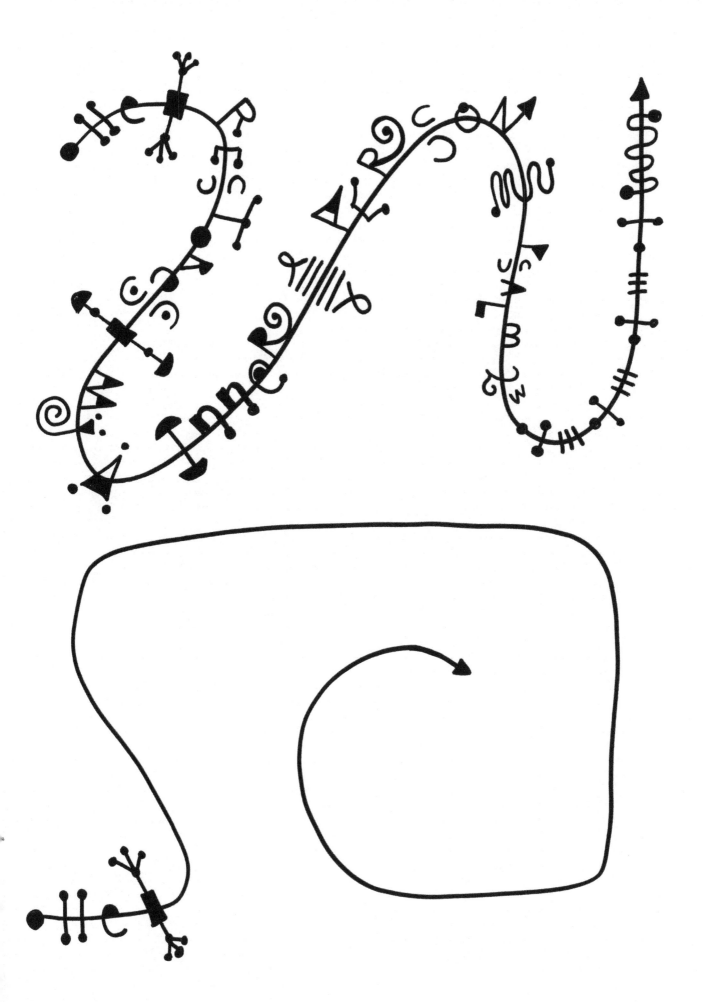

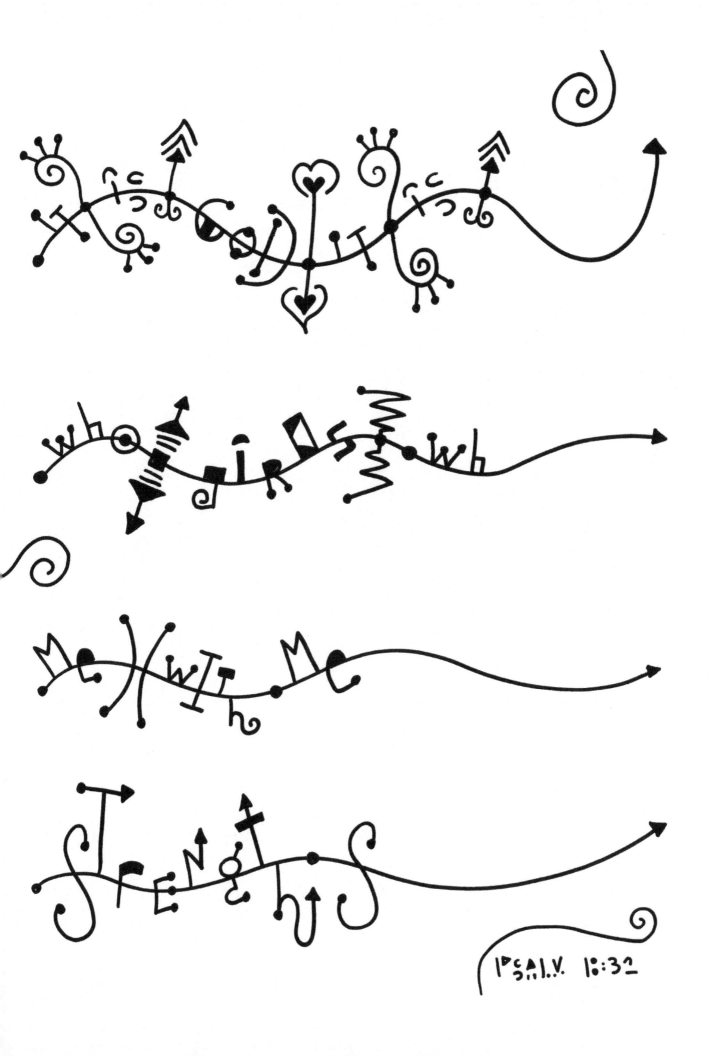

PSALM 18:32

Use logic to complete the verse...

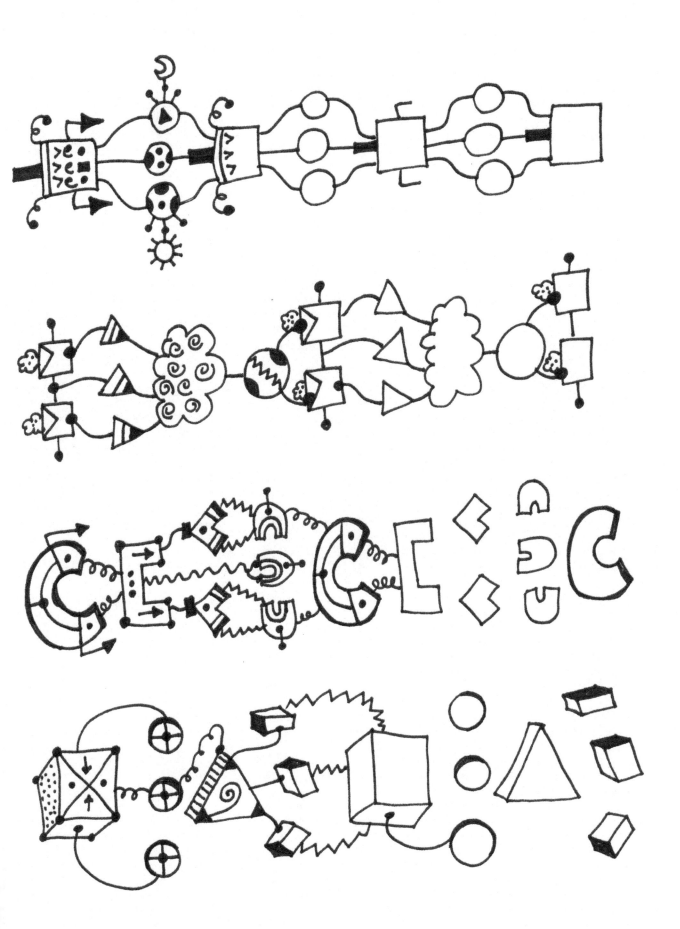

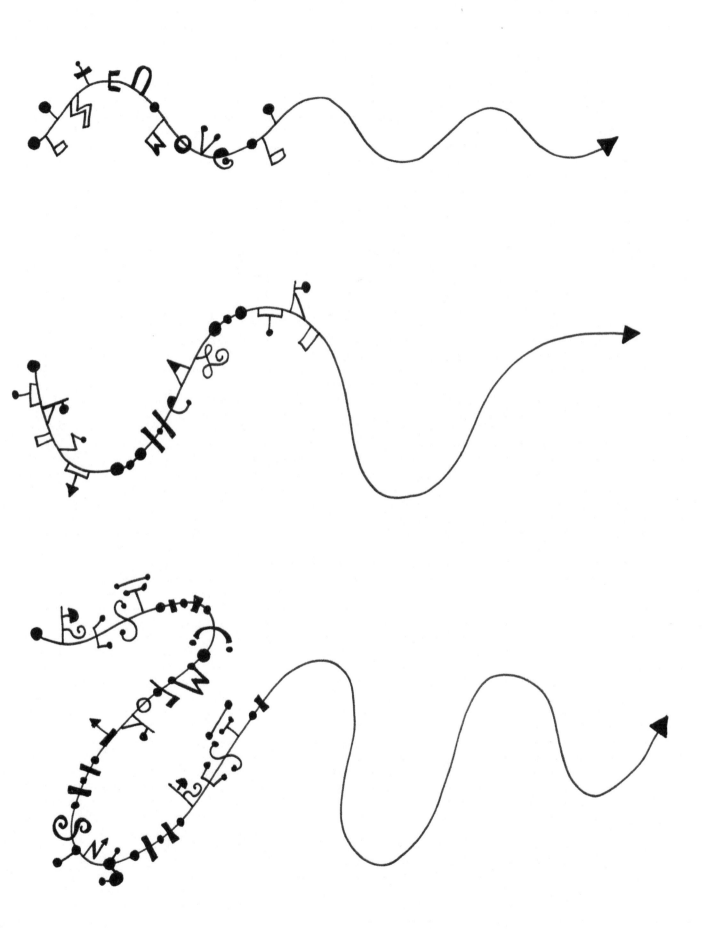

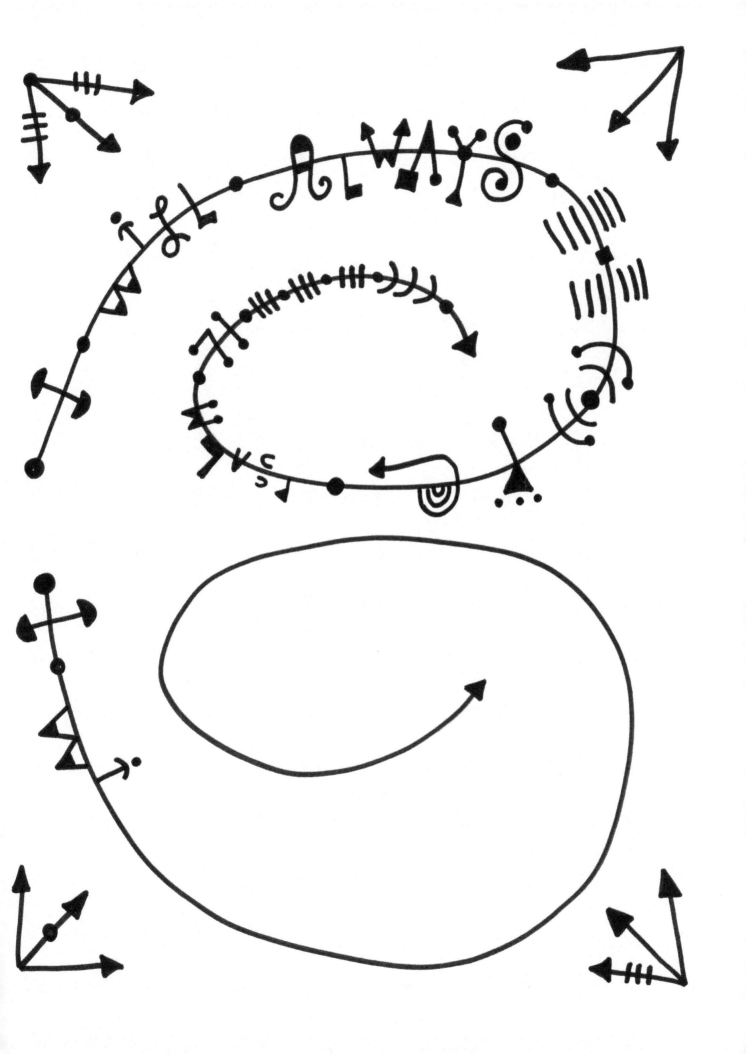

I am like a green olive tree in the House of God

I am like a _____

I am like _____

I am _____

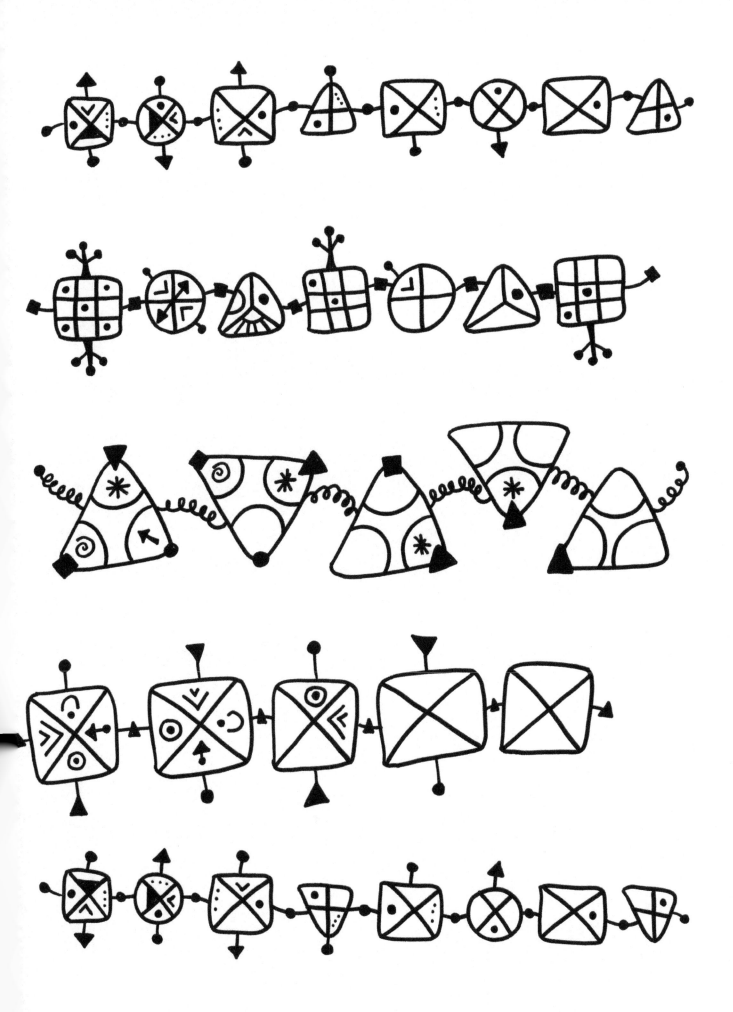

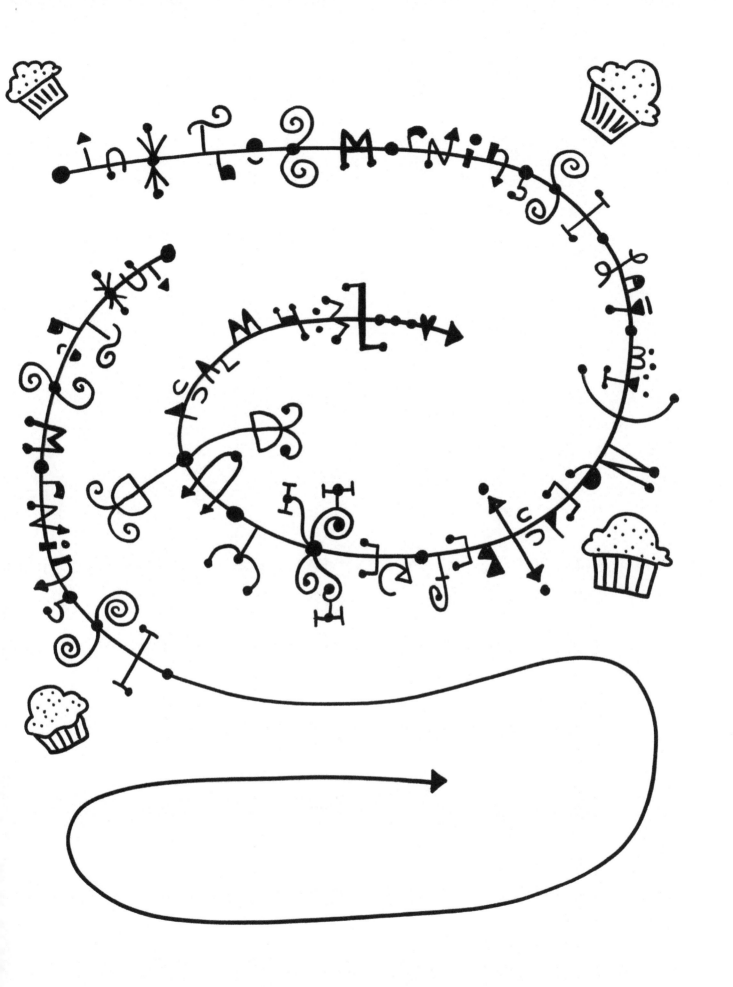

My Soul, Wait in Silence
for God Alone
Psalm 62

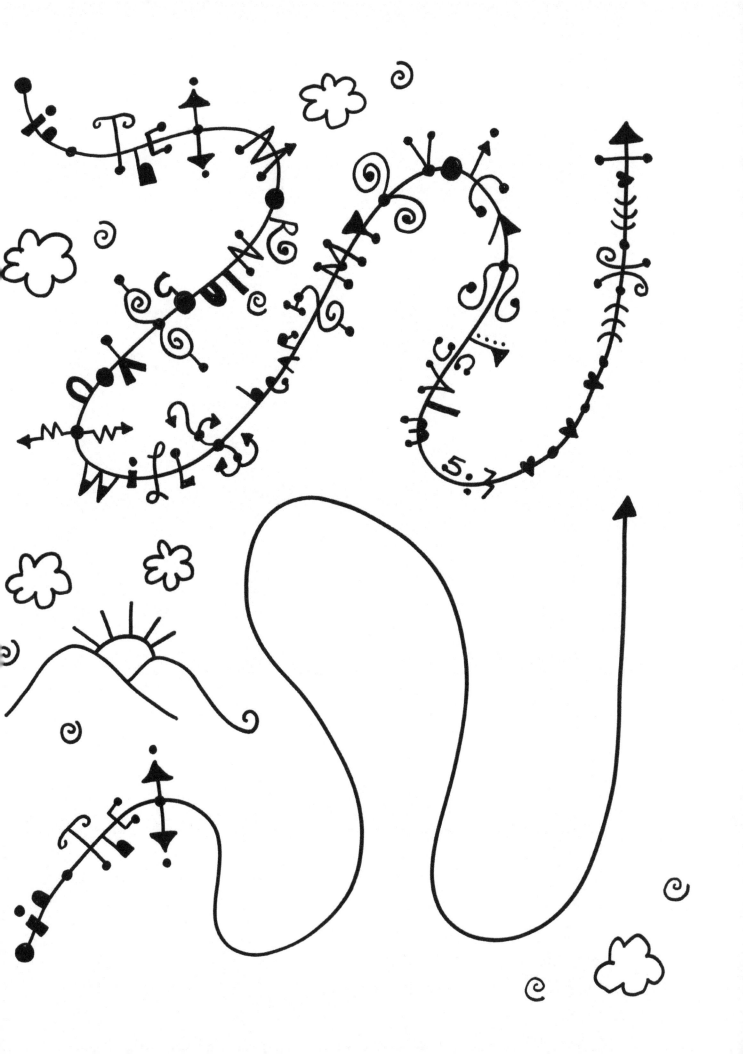

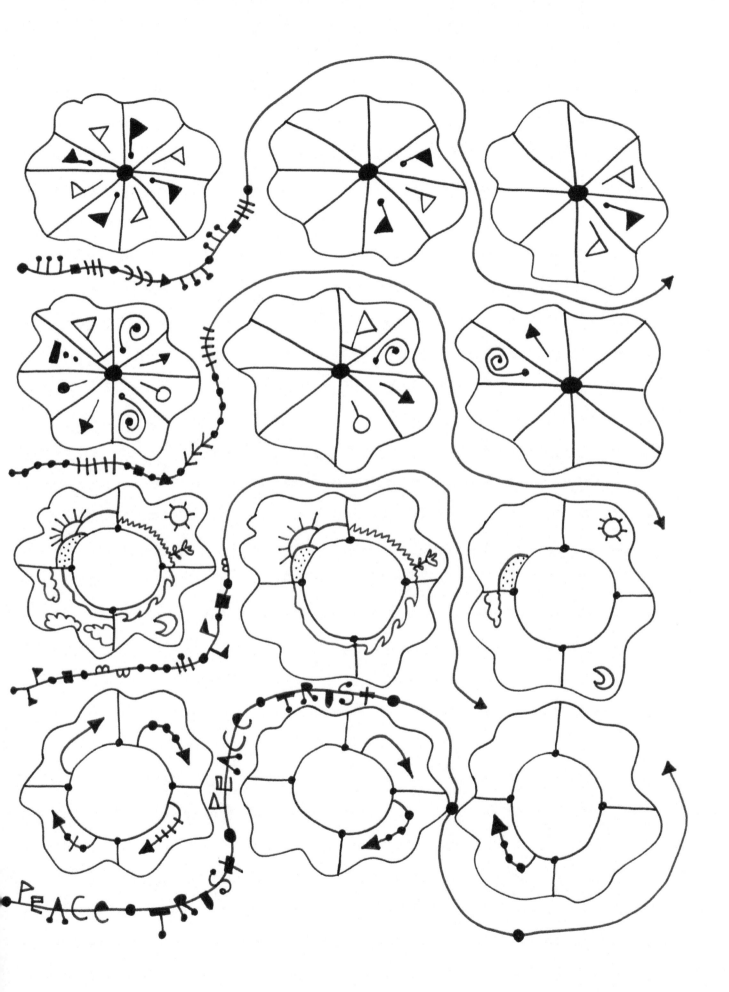

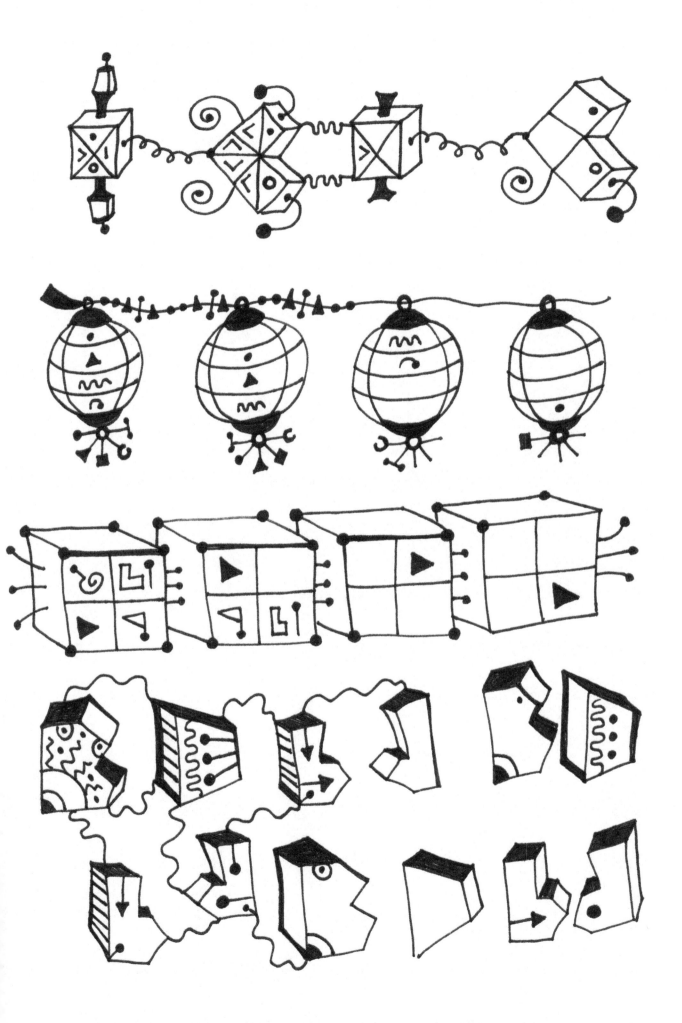

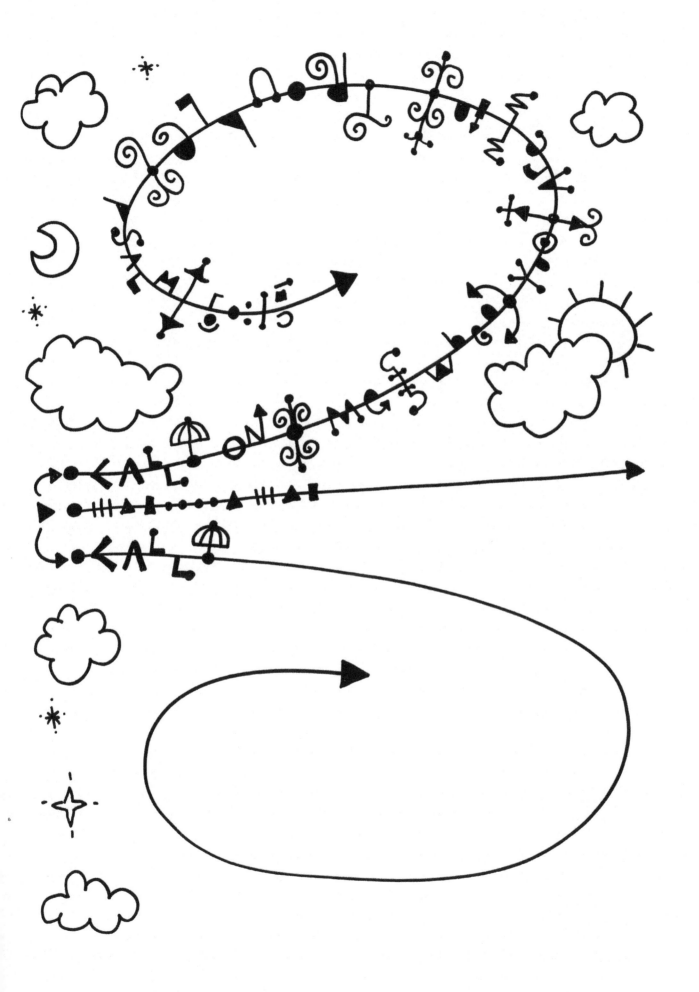

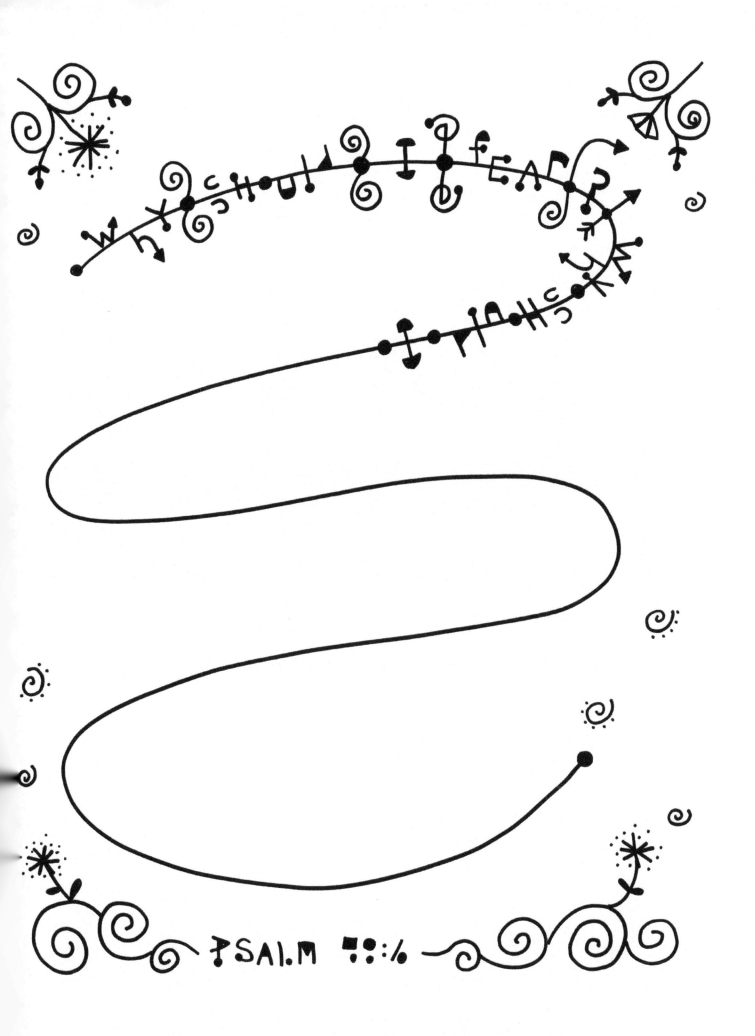

WHY SHOULD I FEAR?

WHY SHOULD I FEAR?

PSALM 49:6

The Thinking Tree

Sarah Janisse Brown

Blog: FunSchoolingWithSarah.com

Bookstore: Funschooling.com